CW00432065

THE TUDOR REMEDY BOOK

curious cures for common complaints

Published by Osborne Books Limited
Unit 1b Everoak Estate, Bromyard Road,
Worcester, WR2 5HN
General Editor: Michael Fardon
Cover Design: Louise Ferebee, Pineapple Publishing
Printed by the Bath Press, Bath

ISBN 1 872962 41 6

Introduction

This little book of remedies, which were current in Tudor times, has been compiled from the celebrated writings of Nicholas Culpeper whose seventeenth century "Complete Herbal" and "English Physician" were popular in many households until late into the nineteenth century.

The remedies have been arranged in alphabetical order of the complaints they were designed to cure - ranging from asthma, through rotting gums, piles and vomits to warts and worms.

It would have been a brave patient who submitted to these remedies, and a lucky one who survived them.

Health Warning

Although the remedies in this book may have worked in past times, they are not recommended for use today.

Contents

Asthma	7
Black Jaundice	9
Bleeding of wounds	10
Breasts that are sore	11
Bruises and scalds	12
Burns and scalds	13
Consumption	14
Courses that are stopped	15
Ears wih boils	16
Ears with almonds	17
Eyes with rheum	18
Eyes hurt with a stroke	19
Eye water	20
Eyes that are blasted	21
Faces with pustules	22
Faces full of red pimples	23
Fever	24
Giddiness	25
Gums with scurvy	26
Gums that are sore	27

Gums that are rotting 28
Hair that is falling off 29
Head purged by gargarisms 30
Head with rheum and the palsy 31
Head with rheum 32
Head-ache 33
Hooping cough 34
Liver infirmities 35
Liver and digestion 36
Liver that is stopped 37
Mouth diseases 38
Mouth with heat and canker 39
Mouth that is sore 40
Nose with polypus 41
Nose cleaning and bleeding 42
Nose with canker 43
Nosebleeds 44
Piles and heart-burn 45
Pimples 46
Stomach infirmities 47
Stomach moisture and heat 48
Stomach stuffing 49

Strain 50
Teeth and their medicines 51
Teeth whiteness 52
Tooth-ache 53
Throat infirmities 54
Throat hoarseness 55
Throat soreness 56
Vomits 57
Warts 59
Worms in the body 60
Wounds 61
Yellow Jaundice 62

Nicholas Culpeper

A Cure for an Asthma or Shortness of Breath

Take a quart of aquae vitae, one ounce of aniseeds bruised, one ounce of liquorice sliced, half a pound of raisins stoned; then let them all steep ten days in the aquae vitae, being well covered up, after which time pour the same off into a bottle, then add two table spoonfuls of fine sugar to the same, and stop it very close for use.

A Remedy for the Asthma and shortness of Breath

Take of the milk of gum ammoniac six ounces, syrup of squills four ounces and a half: mix them together.

This promotes expectoration in a very great degree, and relieves those who are short-winded. It is justly esteemed for its serviceable properties in asthmatic cases, by rarefying and thinning viscid cohesions in the pulmonary vessels. A spoonful is to be taken four or five times every day.

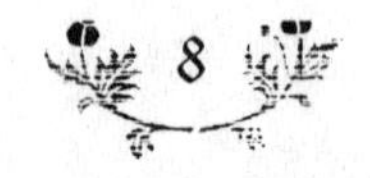

For the Black Jaundice

Take a handful of the long leaves that grow upon artichoke stalks, bruise and put them into a pot with three pints of ale; let the pot stand in a warm place, close covered up, for twelves hours; then take a small glass of this liquor, mixed with half a glass of white wine, for nine mornings together, fasting, and let a drachm of saffron be tied up in a small bit of cloth, and put in the pot amongst the same.

How to stop the bleeding of any Wound

Take burnt leather powdered, bole in powder, dragon's blood in powder: mix some spirits of wine with all these said ingredients, and lay it thereon with soft fine lint.

For sore Breasts

Take a handful of figs, and stamp them well till the kernels are broken, then temper them with a little fresh grease, and apply them to the breast as hot as the patient can endure; it will presently take away the anguish, and if the breast will break, it will break it, else it will cure it without breaking.

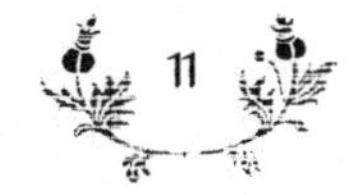

For a Bruise or Scald outwardly

Take one quart of neatsfoot oil, half a pound of red lead, two ounces of bees' wax; boil all these things together 3 hours, during which time you must stir them well; then add to the same one ounce of the oil of elder, let it cool for use, and bathe the part afflicted with the same.

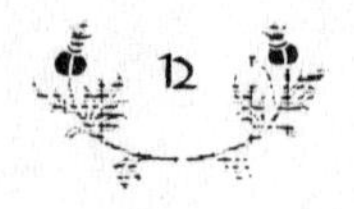

An excellent Remedy for a Burn or Scald

Mix a little lapis calaminaris (which you get at the chemists) in a little snow water, and shake it well together. It doth wonderfully take the fire out of any burn, and you may make as much in the course of the winter as will serve all the year.

A Remedy for a Consumption, if taken in time

Take one handful of horehound, and the same quantity of garden rue, with two pounds of coarse sugar; put these ingredients into two quarts of water, boil them all together until they are reduced to one quart, then take three large table spoonfuls of the same early in the morning fasting.

How to help those whose Courses are stopped

Take two ounces of the grains of paradise, one ounce of long pepper, one ounce of turmeric, and two ounces of steel filings, all in powder; make it into an electuary with a little honey, and take about the size of a walnut night and morning: and two or three times in the course of the day take a wine glass full of the decoction of garden rue, wormwood, horehound, and nettles, for some days.

For a boil in the ear

Boil some milk, and put it into a stone pot with a narrow mouth, and hold the sore ear over the pot whilst the milk is very hot, that the vapour of the milk may ascend into the ear: this is an often approved remedy to take away the pain, and break the boil.

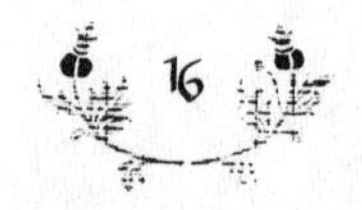

For the falling down of the Almonds of the Ears

Mix a little bole ammoniac in powder, with some Venice turpentine; spread it on sheep's leather as broad as a stay, and then apply the same under the throat from ear to ear.

To draw rheum back from the Eyes

Take an egg and roast it hard, then pull off the shell, and slit it in two, and apply it hot to the nape of the neck, and thou shalt find ease presently.

For a hurt in the Eye with a stroke

Take agrimony, and bruise it very well, and temper it with white wine, and the white of an egg: spread it pretty thick upon a cloth, like a plaster, and apply it to the outside of the eye-lid, and although it be almost out, it will cure it.

An excellent water to clear the Sight

Take of fennel, eyebright, roses, white, celandine, vervain and rue, of each a handful, the liver of a goat chopt small, infuse them well in eyebright-water, then distil them in an alembic, and you shall have a water which will clear the sight beyond comparison.

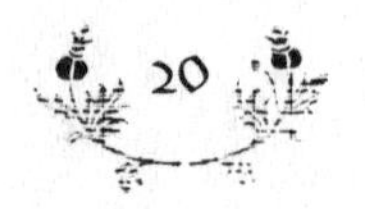

For Eyes that are blasted

Only wear a piece of black sarcenet before thy eyes, and meddle with no medicine; only forbear wine and strong drink.

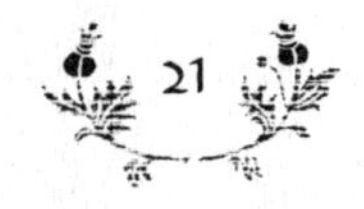

Breaking out of pustules on the Face

It is palpable, that the cause of redness and breaking out of the face is a venomous matter, or filthy vapours ascending from the stomach towards the head; where meeting with a rheum or phlegm thence descending, mix with it, and break out in the face. Therefore let the first intention of cure be to cleanse the stomach.

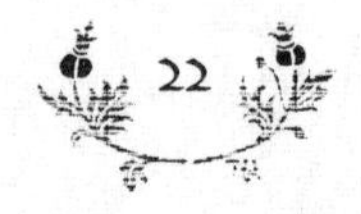

For a face full of red Pimples

Dissolve camphire in vinegar, and mix it, and the vinegar with celandine-water, and wash the face with it: this cured a maid in twenty days, that had been troubled with the infirmity half so many years.

For a Fever

Drink the decoction of camomile, well sweetened with treacle. Take it when you are warm in bed, and sweat two hours.

Pills for Giddiness

Take native cinnabar levigated two drachms, castor and salt of amber, of each one drachm, oil of marjoram fifteen drops, balsam of Peru one dram, syrup of peony a sufficient quantity to make a mass; and from every drachm of it cut off nine pills. The dose is three of them to be taken three times each day.

For a Scurvy in the Gums

Take cloves, and boil them in rose-water, then dry them, and beat them to powder, and rub the gums with the powder, and drink the decoction in the morning fasting an hour after it. Use red rose water, for that is the best.

For the Soreness in the Gums

Make sage tea, and dissolve therein a little alum; dip a cloth therein, and rub your gums with the same. If you wish to make your teeth white, mix a little burnt alum with six spoonfuls of honey, and two spoonfuls of the juice of celandine, and rub your teeth with the same.

For rotting and consuming of the Gums

Take sage-water, and wash your mouth with it every morning, and afterwards rub your mouth with a sage-leaf.

For the falling off of the Hair

Beat linseeds very well, and mix them with salad-oil; and when you have well mixed them, anoint the head therewith, and in three or four times using it will help you.

To purge the Head

The head is purged by gargarisms, of which mustard, in my opinion, is excellent, and therefore a spoonful of mustard put into the mouth is excellent for one that is troubled with the lethargy: also the head is purged by sneezing; but be sure, if you would keep your brain clear, keep your stomach clean.

For a rheum in the Head, and the Palsy

Take a red onion, and bruise it well, and boil it in a little verjuice, and put thereto a little clarified honey, and a great spoonful of good mustard; when it is well boiled, raise the sick upright, and let him receive the smell up his nose twice a day whilst it is very hot.

For a rheum in the Head

Boil pimpernel well in wine, and drink a draught of the wine in the evening hot, but in the morning cold.

Another . . .

Stew onions in a close pot, and bathe the head and mouth, and nose therewith.

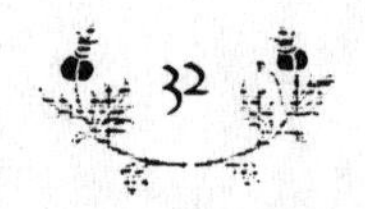

An Essence for the Head-Ache

Head-aches are sometimes caused from an obnoxious vapour ascending out of the stomach, which in this case must be cleansed by proper remedies; but for common head-aches, take of French brandy, or rectified spirit of wine, one quart; put it into a strong bottle, and add one ounce of camphire, cut small, a quarter of an ounce of the essence of lemon, and two ounces of the strongest volatile spirit of sal ammoniac; stop the bottle quite close, and shake it three or four times a day, for a week.

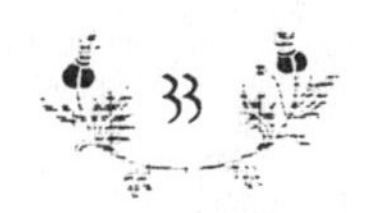

Remedy for Hooping or Chin-Cough

Take flour of Benjamin, and strained opium, of each two drachms, camphire two scruples, essential oil of aniseeds half a drachm, rectified spirits of wine one quart, four ounces of powdered liquorice, and four ounces of honey; then digest and strain off the elixir.

Of The Liver, And Its Infirmities

A caution

If the liver be too hot, it usually proceeds from too much blood, and is known by redness of urine, the pulse is swift, the veins great and full, the spittle, mouth, and tongue, seem sweeter than they used to be. The cure is letting blood in the right arm.

To cause the Liver well to digest

Take oil of wormwood, and so much mastich in powder as will make it into a poultice, lay it warm to your right side.

A caution

If the liver be stopped, the face will swell, and you shall be as sure to have a pain in your right side, as though you had it there already.

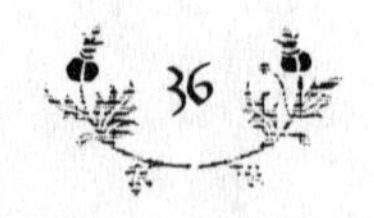

For stoppage of the Liver

Use garden-thyme in all your drinks and broths, it will prevent stoppages before they come, and cure them after they are come.

For the liver

The liver of a hare dried, and beaten into powder, cures all the diseases of the liver of man.

Of The Mouth, And Its Diseases

A Caution

Whosoever would keep their mouth, or tongue, or nose, or eyes, or ears, or teeth, from pain or infirmities, let them often use sneezing; for, indeed, most of the infirmities, if not all, which infest those parts, proceed from rheum.

For extreme heat of the Mouth

Take rib-wort, and boil it in red wine, and hold the decoction as warm in your mouth as you can endure it.

For a Canker in the Mouth

Wash the teeth often with verjuice.

For a sore Mouth

Take the juice of plantain, and rose-water mixed with the same, and frequently wash your mouth; and if your gums are sore, take gun-powder, roche-alum, bole ammoniac, and honey, of each an equal quantity; mix them well together, and when you rub your gums with the same, let the rheum run out of your mouth.

For Polypus; or a flesby substance growing in the Nose

Take the juice of ivy, and make a tent with a little cotton, the which dip in the juice and put it up in the nostril.

To cleanse the Nose

Snuff up the juice of red beet-root: it will cleanse not only the nose, but also the head: this is a singular remedy for such as are troubled with hard congealed stuff in their nostrils.

For Bleeding at the Nose

Bind the arms and legs as hard as you can with a piece of tape-ribboning; that, perhaps, may call back the blood.

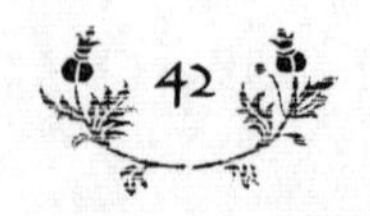

For a Canker in the Nose

Boil strong ale till it be thick; if the canker be in the outside of the nose, spread it as a plaster, and apply it; if in the inside, make a tent of a linen rag, and put it up the nostril.

Another . . .

The water of adder's-tongue snuffed up the nose is very good for the Polypus: but it were better, in my opinion, to keep a rag continually moistened with it in the nose.

For Bleeding at the Nose

Take amber and bruise into gross powder, put it upon a chaffing-dish of coals, and receive the smoke up into the nose with a funnel.

Another . . .

When no other means will stop the bleeding at the nose, it has been known that it hath been stopped by opening a vein in the ear.

A Cure for the Piles or Sores

Eat rosemary and sage with bread and butter, and apply wheat flour and honey, by way of plaister.

For the Heart-Burn

The salts of tartar taken in a little water is a cure for the heart-burn. You may mix equal quantity of magnesia with the same if you please.

How to take away little red Pimples from the Face

Take two ounces of lemon juice, two ounces of rose water, two drachms of silver suppliment, mix them into an ointment, and rub your face with the same at going to bed, and when you get up in the morning rub your face with fresh butter, and then rub the same clean off.

Of The Stomach, And Its Infirmities

A caution

Infirmities of the stomach usually proceed from surfeiting.

Let such as have weak stomachs avoid all sweet things, as honey, sugar, and the like; milk, cheese, and all fat meats, let him not eat till he is hungry, nor drink before he is dry: let him avoid anger, sadness, much travel, and all fried meats: let him not vomit by any means, nor eat when he is hot.

For moisture of the Stomach

Take a drachm of galanga, in powder, every morning in a draught of that wine you like best.

For heat of the Stomach

Swallow four or five grains of Mastich every night going to bed.

A Remedy for a Loading and Stuffing at the Stomach, causing a loss of Appetite

R. Calomel, ppt. gr. xx. Ext. Cathart. ʒss. m. ft. pilul. No. x. capt. duas altern. noct.
If you cannot read this excellent prescription, the chemist can make it up for you.

A Remedy for a Strain

Take the oil of swallows, the oil of peter, and the oil of turpentine, of each an equal quantity, mix them well together, and anoint the part afflicted with the same.

Of The Teeth, And Their Medicines

A Caution

If you will keep your teeth from rotting, or aching, wash your mouth continually every morning with juice of lemons, and afterwards rub your teeth either with a sage-leaf, or else with a little nutmeg in powder; also wash your mouth with a little fair water after meats; for the only way to keep teeth sound, and free from pain is to keep them clean.

To keep Teeth white

Dip a little piece of white cloth in vinegar of quinces, and rub your gums with it, for it is of a gallant binding quality, and not only makes the teeth white, but also strengthens the gums, fastens the teeth, and also causeth a sweet breath.

To fasten the Teeth

Seethe the roots of vervain in old wine, and wash your teeth often with them, and it will fasten them.

For the Tooth-ache

Take the inner rind of an elder-tree, and bruise it, and put thereto a little pepper, and make it into balls, and hold them between the teeth that ache.

Of The Throat, And Its Infirmities

A caution

Diseases in the throat, most commonly proceed of rheum descending from the head upon the trachea arteria, or wind-pipe; in such cases there is many times no other cure than first to purge the body of phlegm, and then the head of rheum.

For Hoarseness

Take of sugar so much as will fill a common taster, then put so much rectified spirit of wine to it as will just wet it; eat this up at night going to bed: use this three or four times together.

Another . . .

If the body be feverish, use the former medicine as before, only use oil of sweet almonds, or for want of it, the best salad-oil instead of spirit of wine.

For the Sore Throat

Take notice that bleeding is good in all inflammations, therefore in this.

It were very convenient that a syrup and an ointment of orpine were always ready in the house for such occasions; for I know no better remedy for the quinsey, than to drink the one, and anoint the throat with the other.

Emetic Tartar Vomit

Dissolve 4 grains of emetic tartar in half a pint of hot water, stir it about well: when cold it is fit for use. Take 2 table-spoonfuls every quarter of an hour till it operates; after which no more of the vomit must be taken. Drink a small cup of gruel, or weak camomile tea after every puke. A pint of gruel, or tea, is generally sufficient. To settle the stomach, drink a little weak brandy and water, and lie down half an hour.

The design of giving the vomit in the manner above described, is in order that it may work in the most gentle manner possible. If it

operates two, or three, or four times, it is sufficient. Violent vomits are often attended with dangerous consequences; whereas gentle ones may be repeated 2 or 3 times a week if necessary.

If a vomit works too violently, drink moderately of weak brandy and water, and apply a raw onion, cut in two, to the pit of the stomach.

The best time for taking a vomit is in a morning fasting. But in cases where no time is to be lost, it may be taken at eleven o' clock, or in the evening.

Emetic tartar is one of the best medicines known at this day.

How to cure Warts

Go into the field and take a black snail, and rub the warts with the snail nine times one way, and then nine times another, and then stick that said snail upon a black-thorn, and the warts will waste. I have also known a black snail cure corns, being laid thereon as a plaister. If you have what is called blood or bleeding warts, then take a piece of raw beef, that never had any salt, and rub them with the same, just in the same manner as you used the snail above mentioned; after this operation is performed, you must bury the piece of beef in the earth.

How to kill Worms or Bot-worms in the body

Take half a glass of brandy, and put therein as much fine sulphur as will lay on a shilling, and mix them together; then burn a bit of bread crust in the fire till it is black, chew the same in your mouth for about five minutes, after which put it out again, and then immediately take the above-mentioned medicine early in the morning.

How to make salve for all Wounds

Take one pound of hog's lard, three ounces of white lead, three ounces of red lead, three ounces of bee's wax, two ounces of black rosin, and four ounces of common turpentine; all these ingredients must be put together in a pan, and boil three quarters of an hour; the turpentine to be put in just before it is done enough, and give it a gentle boil afterwards. This is an excellent salve for burns, old sores, or ulcers, as it first draws, then heals afterwards; it is excellent for all wounds, and ought to be always kept in your house.

How to cure the Yellow Jaundice without Medicine, or giving any thing to the patient whatsoever

Take the patient's morning urine, and put the same into a bottle; and take a small piece of saffron, and tie it up in a fine piece of muslin, and put the same in the bottle amongst the said urine; and only desire the patient wholly to abstain from drinking either milk or malt liquor for one month. Proved a great number of times.

This prescription alone is worth more money than the price of this book.

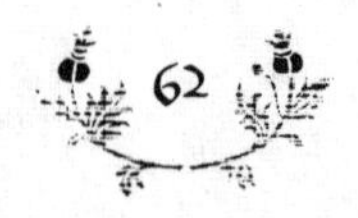